Little Bunny Bobkin

Little Bunny Bobkin

by James Riordan

Illustrated by Tim Warnes

ORCHARD BOOKS

For Benedict and Sebastian
JR

For Sally
TW

ORCHARD BOOKS
96 Leonard Street, London EC2A 4RH
Orchard Books, Australia
14 Mars Road, Lane Cove, NSW 2066
Text © James Riordan 1998
Illustrations © Tim Warnes 1998
ISBN 1 86039 148 6 (hardback)
ISBN 1 84121 049 8 (paperback)
First published in Great Britain in 1998
This edition published in 1999
The right of James Riordan to be identified as the author
and Tim Warnes to be identified as the illustrator
of this Work has been asserted by them in accordance with the
Copyright, Designs and Patents Act 1988.
A CIP catalogue record of this book is available
from the British Library
Printed in Singapore
3 5 7 9 10 8 6 4 2

Mother Rabbit had a whole burrowful of bunnies.
     The eldest was Misha. Then came Sasha, Masha and Natasha.

Last of all was
Little Bunny Bobkin.

Like all young rabbits they liked to hop and skip together. Only Little Bobkin did not join in. He was learning to count.

He sat gazing at himself in a puddle and he counted:
"One twitchy nose.
One fluffy tail.
Two long ears.
Two big bright eyes."

A ladybird came crawling by. Little Bunny Bobkin was so happy; now he could count the spots on her wings.

"One spot, two spots..." he began.

But before he could say 'three', the ladybird had flown away home.

Little Bunny Bobkin stood on his hind legs and glanced about.

Beside the stream, he saw a nest with four fluffy ducklings.

"One duckling, two ducklings, three ducklings..." he began.
But before he could say 'four', Mother Duck appeared.
"What do you mean by bothering my babies!"
she quacked crossly.
And she shooed him away.

As Little Bunny Bobkin hopped off, he spotted a clump of scarlet poppies in a cornfield. Here was something he could count!

"One poppy, two poppies, three poppies, four ..." he began.

But before he could say 'five', a swarm of honey bees appeared. They bustled and buzzed and settled in the poppy cups. A big bee buzzed in Bobkin's ear.

"Out of our way! We must collect pollen from these poppies to make honey."

And the honey bees chased him away.

Poor Little Bunny Bobkin! Would nobody help him learn to count?

Then he spied some dandelion fluff floating in the air and he chased after it happily.

"One fluff, two fluffs, three fluffs, four; five fluffs, six..."

But he did not notice that he was wandering deeper and deeper into the wild, wild, wood.

It started to rain. Hurrying to shelter in the
hollow of a tree, he smiled a great big smile:
for there he saw a familiar sight – furry tails,
gleaming eyes and tawny toes.

As he squeezed inside, he began to count.
"One, two, three noses;
 four, five, six eyes;
 seven, eight, nine ..."
But before he could count all the toes ...

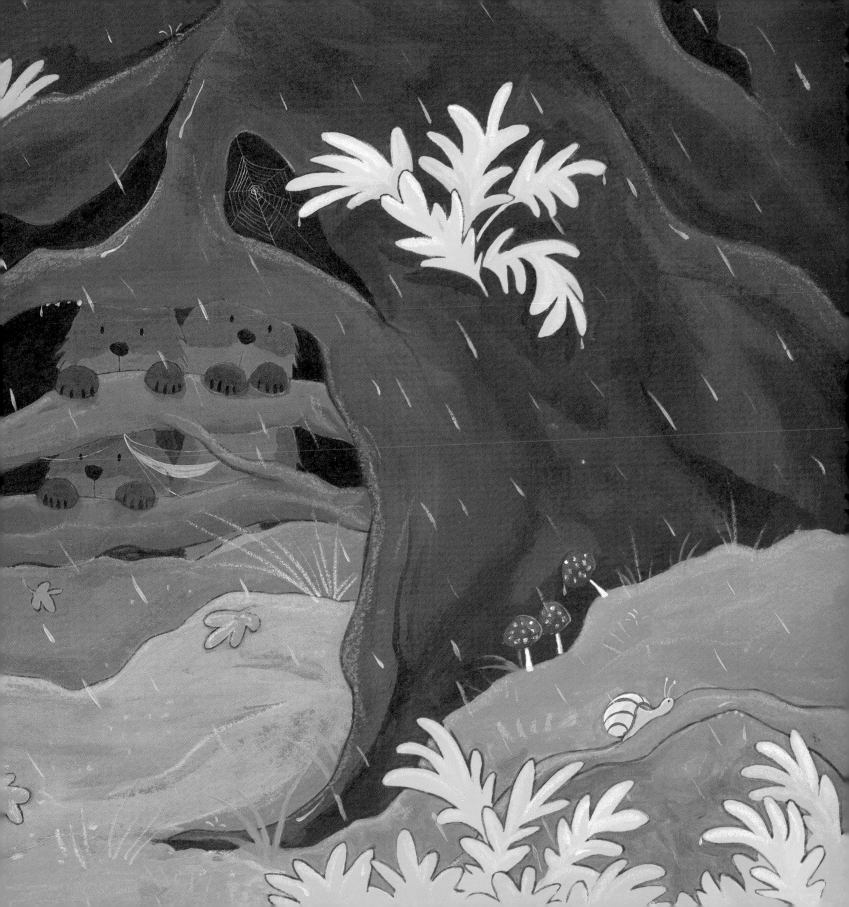

"Welcome to my den, bunny rabbit!" hissed a voice. "You will make a tasty meal."

Standing behind him was Mother Fox.

Then he saw that the noses were long, the eyes glinted in the gloom, and the toes had sharp claws!

This wasn't his burrow, and these weren't his brothers and sisters. He was in the Foxes' den!

Little Bunny Bobkin knew that he would have to think quickly: he didn't want to be eaten for lunch!

"Mother Fox," he said in a small voice, "will you teach me to count before you eat me?"

Mother Fox saw no harm in that, she liked counting.

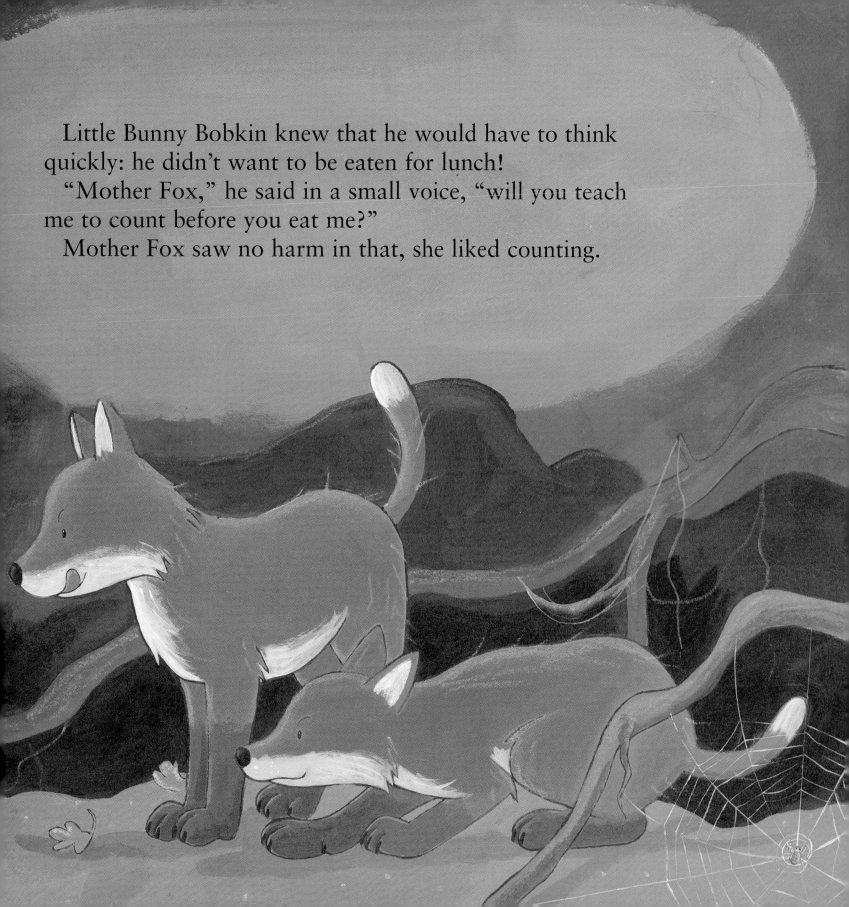

"Now, let's see," Mother Fox began, licking her lips.
"One plump little bunny with two fluffy ears,
 Three little foxes, so hungry, poor dears,
 Four sprigs of parsley, fresh and green,
 Five new potatoes, peeled and clean,
 Six tasty turnips with seven broad beans,
 Eight white leeks and lots of greens,
 Nine juicy carrots, just right for the pot,
 Ten cups of water and what have we got?
"Rabbit stew!" yelled the fox cubs.

"But, Mother Fox," said Little Bunny Bobkin, "first you will need ten bones to flavour the broth. You must have some at the back of your den."

"Yes, some delicious bones would make a tasty stew!" said Mother Fox, and she disappeared into the far corner of the den.

Little Bunny Bobkin could hear her counting as she gathered the bones together.

"One bone, two bones, three bones, four; five bones, six bones, seven bones, more..."
He didn't wait to hear her finish. With a flick of his tail he dashed out of the den.

"eight bones, nine bones, TEN BONES!"

But Little Bunny Bobkin was on his way, racing home for all he was worth.

He squeezed into the burrow. How glad he was to be home!
And he counted ...
"One cosy burrow and one Mother Rabbit.
Four little bunnies and Bobkin makes five."

Mother Rabbit took him onto her lap, rocking
him to and fro as he told her his story.

It was warm and cosy in his mother's arms,
and he smiled to himself as he thought how he
had fooled the fox.

Through the open doorway he could see a patch of dark
blue sky, with twinkling stars and a crescent moon.

"Now no one will stop me counting," he thought.

"One bright moon," he began.

Then he started on the stars.

"One star, two stars, three stars, four;
five stars, six stars, seven stars, more;
eight stars ... nine stars ..."

But before Little Bunny Bobkin could
count the tenth star his voice trailed away
until there was no sound at all.

"Hush," murmured Mother Rabbit
to her bunnies, "Little Bunny Bobkin
is fast asleep."